# Buddy's C

By Dr. Bernie S. Siegel
Illustrated by Mari Gayatri Stein

Order this book online at www.trafford.com/07-1199
or email orders@trafford.com

Most Trafford titles are also available at major online book retailers.

Note for Librarians: A cataloguing record for this book is available from Library
and Archives Canada at www.collectionscanada.ca/amicus/index-e.html

Printed in Victoria, BC, Canada.

ISBN: 978-1-4251-3227-9

*We at Trafford believe that it is the responsibility of us all, as both individuals
and corporations, to make choices that are environmentally and socially sound.
You, in turn, are supporting this responsible conduct each time you purchase a
Trafford book, or make use of our publishing services. To find out how you are
helping, please visit www.trafford.com/responsiblepublishing.html*

*Our mission is to efficiently provide the world's finest, most comprehensive
book publishing service, enabling every author to experience success.
To find out how to publish your book, your way, and have it available
worldwide, visit us online at www.trafford.com/10510*

www.trafford.com

**North America & international**
toll-free: 1 888 232 4444 (USA & Canada)
phone: 250 383 6864 ♦ fax: 250 383 6804
email: info@trafford.com

**The United Kingdom & Europe**
phone: +44 (0)1865 722 113 ♦ local rate: 0845 230 9601
facsimile: +44 (0)1865 722 868 ♦ email: info.uk@trafford.com

10 9 8 7 6 5 4 3

For anyone who has ever lost a loved one.

The morning after my son Simon's ninth birthday party, I was stretched out on the sofa with our dog Ike when Simon came over and sat down beside me.

"Dad, yesterday when I was blowing out my birthday candles you had a sad expression on your face that I've never seen before. What were you thinking about?"

I explained that his party stirred up a lot of memories. I told him that when I was nine years old, I was diagnosed with a type of cancer called leukemia, and everyone was worried about me. I hadn't shared this story with Simon because I didn't want to frighten or upset him. I asked him if he would like to hear my story now.

"Yes, please Dad."

I hadn't been feeling well for weeks, so my parents took me to our pediatrician who performed a number of tests. When he told the family that I had leukemia, they were devastated. My parents and my little sister, Rose, didn't know what to do.

"I'm so sorry Dad." Simon gave his dad a big hug.

"Thanks Simon. I needed that. You can never have too many hugs. The doctor started me on chemotherapy which made my hair fall out and left me feeling even weaker and sicker. I missed a lot of school and wasn't allowed to play with my friends, because the treatment knocked out my ability to fight infections. It was pretty depressing to say the least."

"Gee Dad you must have felt very scared and lonely."

On one particularly rough day, my parents asked me if there was anything they could do for me. I told them I had always wanted a dog to keep me company and I sure could use one now. My doctor said a dog was okay as long as it was checked by a veterinarian first to be sure it was healthy. My parents didn't do anything about it because they really didn't want a dog in the house. That's when God stepped in.

"What do you mean Dad?"

One afternoon after my treatment, I was lying in our hammock on the front porch when I felt something warm and wet rub against my hands and face. I thought it was my sister kidding around, but when I opened my eyes there was a scrawny looking fluffy brown dog staring at me. He looked so hungry that I hurried into the house to get him a piece of left over chicken.

"Hey little Buddy here's a treat for you," I said. I sat and watched him gobble it down. "Mom quick," I yelled. "Come outside. I have a surprise for you."

When she came out, I introduced her to my new friend and told her his name was Buddy. She took one look at Buddy and said, "Hmmm. We'll wait until your Dad gets home before we make any decisions."

When my Dad arrived, he didn't know what to do. I told my folks that God had sent Buddy, and he was family now. My Dad smiled, put his hand on my shoulder and said, "All right Simon, I can see how much he means to you. Buddy can become part of our family if the vet says he's healthy."

The next day, we went to see Doctor Cary, the veterinarian. As he examined Buddy, I saw his expression fade from a smile to a frown. He turned to us and said softly, "I am so sorry to have to tell you this, knowing what you are all going through, but Buddy has enlarged lymph nodes in his neck. I would like to keep him overnight for some tests."

"That must have been terrible, Dad."

"Yes, it was Simon."

We all went home. No one said anything. I knew they were thinking that Buddy probably wouldn't make it, and they were worried about me too.

When Buddy's tests were completed, we returned to the animal hospital. Doctor Cary said that Buddy had a kind of cancer called lymphoma and asked us if we wanted him to start treatment. I yelled, "Yes" before my folks could say anything.

They looked at each other, at Buddy, and then at me and said, "Okay, let's make an appointment for Buddy's first chemotherapy treatment, and then we can all get well together."

When we brought Buddy home, he was so happy that he started running around the living room, jumping into my lap trying to get me to play with him. It was obvious he wasn't worried about anything but was just trying to enjoy the day.

"Maybe Buddy knows something we don't," I told my parents. "We need to start having more fun each day. Let's try to make every day a chocolate ice cream day."

After that, whenever something would happen, we would ask, "What would Buddy do?" He truly became our teacher and made us aware of the many things for which we should be grateful each and every day. He made us realize that all the side effects of cancer are not bad.

"That's wonderful, Dad, he sounds like he was a wise dog and a great coach."

"Yes, Simon. You're right, and the best is yet to come."

In short order the story got around about the little boy and his dog both having cancer, and the local newspaper came to interview our family. When the article appeared in the paper, it described how I was hoping for a bone marrow transplant but that no matching donor had been found. Well everyone within fifty miles of our town showed up to be tested, and they found a matching donor for me.

"Wow, Dad. If Buddy hadn't adopted you, you might never have been in the newspaper and found a donor."

"That's right, Simon. Buddy was my Godsend and helped me find a new life. I learned that life is all about beginnings."

The next week I was admitted to the hospital. The treatment was really rough. The doctors were very discouraged and preparing my family for the worst. I told my folks I didn't want any more treatments, and I wanted to say goodbye to Buddy. My folks asked the doctor if they could bring Buddy to the hospital for a last visit.

The doctor was really nice. He transferred my bed from the bone marrow unit to a private room where my parents and Buddy could see me. At that point I was hardly moving or talking or aware of what was going on around me anymore. My folks told me later that when Buddy came into my room, and before anyone could stop him, he pulled the leash out of my mom's hand, jumped up on the bed, lay down next to me and started licking my face. I reached over to pet him and said, "Hi Buddy. Thanks for coming. I love you."

My folks said everyone in the room started to cry.

From that moment on, my condition began to improve. The doctors had a white coat made for Buddy to wear when he visited, and they embroidered the words "Buddy, MD" on the jacket. They said in this case, the MD stood for My Dog.

In a few weeks I was home again playing with Buddy and taking him for his treatment too. Buddy made my life so much more fun. We took hikes, played games, and went fishing together.

One day, while fishing, I tripped on a rock and fell into the pond. Buddy jumped right in and pulled me to shore. When we got home my mom asked me why we were both soaking wet. I told her how Buddy had rescued me.

From that day on my mom changed all the rules. Now, wherever I went Buddy was allowed to go too. At night he would cuddle up next to me in bed, and in the morning he would walk me to the front gate where we waited for the school bus together. Every afternoon he would be sitting at the gate waiting to walk me home. My Mom told me she was sure Buddy could tell time, because he always went to the front door and barked when the bus was due.

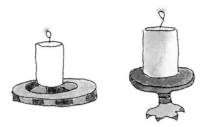

One afternoon, when I got off the bus, there was no Buddy waiting for me. I called his name and when he didn't appear I knew something was wrong. I ran home as fast as I could. My Dad was sitting on the front steps waiting for me.

"Son, Buddy's condition took a turn for the worst. We had to take him to the hospital," my dad said.

I cried all the way to the animal hospital. I could see how hard it was for Buddy to breathe. He licked my hand while I petted him gently and told him how sorry I was, and that if he needed to go I would understand. I told him our love would keep us together forever. Then I put my head down next to his, and he licked my tears.

A few days later, we buried Buddy by the front gate with my note that read: Together Forever.

One day Doctor Cary stopped by and asked how I was doing. I said that every time I got off the school bus, I started to cry and wished Buddy were there to greet me.

We sat down and talked for what seemed like a really long time. He asked if I knew why dogs have shorter lives than people. I told him dogs know how to love and forgive, so they don't need all that time to learn. He said that my sadness and tears were normal, and when I felt ready I should ask Buddy to help me find a way to turn my loss into a blessing. He said our love was immortal and like a rainbow bridge which connects the land of the living and the land of the dead.

I went to bed early that night, and prayed for Buddy to show me the way. That night an Angel appeared in my bedroom and whispered, "Do not be afraid. I am a messenger sent here to tell you that death is not the end. It is like a graduation, a commencement, and a new beginning. I have come to help you to understand why."

She took my hand and led me across the rainbow bridge to a place filled with light. She told me, "In animal heaven we have a special day each year when we celebrate the new arrivals. I brought you here to watch their parade. You will see the animals are all perfect again, each one bearing a bright candle."

As I watched the parade I saw a dog with an unlit, dark candle. I mentioned it to the Angel and she said, "Why don't you go and light it for him?"

As I approached the dog, I saw that it was Buddy.

"Buddy your candle is dark," I told him. "Let me light it for you."

"They do, but your tears keep putting it out."

After lighting Buddy's candle I promised him that whenever I missed him and felt like crying, I would think of our love instead so that his candle would keep burning brightly.

Before Buddy and the Angel waved goodbye, the Angel showed me an enormous room full of candles and said, "When a soul is ready to be reborn they put their candle here and it starts to burn up. Each candle's length represents someone's remaining life time. Some are sadly very short and others thankfully quite long. Someday your soul dog, Buddy, will return, and the two of you will be reunited."

Then Buddy and the Angel crossed over the Rainbow Bridge, their candles aglow.

Although I never told my folks about my dream, they were happy to see the change in me. I started volunteering at the animal shelter and spending more time helping my folks around the farm.

A few months later when my mom dropped me off at the shelter, one of the puppies ran over and began jumping up and down and licking my hand. When I held him, he licked my nose too.

My mom came to pick me up, and I showed her the puppy. "Simon, he acts like you are old buddies."

"Look mom," I pointed out to her. "He has a spot on his nose like Buddy did. Can I take my new buddy home with me?"

My mom thought for a minute and said, "Yes, Simon. But he will need a name that will make him feel special too."

R emembering that my mom had said one of the reasons she didn't want a dog was because it would shed little bits of fur all over the furniture, I named my new friend, Furphy. I carried my new buddy home, and when I held him close and felt his soft fur tickling my nose, I heard a voice whisper, "Together, Forever."

"Well Simon, now you know why candles are so special to me and why your birthday candles reminded me of my ninth birthday. Candles remind me to live every moment to the fullest, to burn up and not out, and to always let our inner light shine so we can be beacons for others."

"Dad, thanks. I'll remember that next time I am sad, and I won't let my tears put out any candles either," said my son.

"Simon, please understand tears are not wrong. They may soften our pain, but grief and tears are not meant to take over our lives. We are here to show compassion to each other in times of difficulty. So live and learn and remember the candles, what keeps them eternally lit, and that the only light of permanence is love. The lesson I learned from Buddy and my leukemia is what made me want to be a doctor and care for kids with cancer."

"Thanks for sharing your story Dad. I think I'm going to be a veterinarian when I grow up, so I can help animals and learn from them too, like you did. Maybe we can share a waiting room where the animals teach and heal everyone."

## MARI GAYATRI STEIN

Mari Gayatri Stein's insightful words and drawings have delighted readers for over twenty years. Her whimsical illustrations and articles have been published in numerous collaborative book efforts, magazines, newspapers and journals. Seven of her highly acclaimed books were both written and illustrated by Mari. Her recent books, *Unleashing Your Inner Dog: Your Best Friend's Guide to Life* and *The Buddha Smiles* are stories about love, spirit and heart, doused with humor, irony and hope.

Clarissa Pinkola Estés describes her work as, "Witty and charming, artful little gems. Mari has universal insight into what people find funny."

Mari lives with her husband and their two canine companions on an organic farm and bamboo sanctuary in the Northwest. She teaches yoga and meditation, has created a new line of whimsical greeting cards, a soon to be released picture book, entitled *Puddle Moon*, and is goofy-in-love when it comes to animals of all kinds.

CONTACT MARI AT: whimsicalmari@hotmail.com

MARI'S DEDICATION:

To the peace and happiness of all beings, in all realms, in all forms. Special thanks to my soul mate, Robert, who is my anchor, my dear friend Andrea Hurst, and to my constant sidekicks Snowflake and Mumbles who succor me with their infinite kisses and wags.

BERNIE'S DEDICATION AND SPECIAL THANKS:

This book is dedicated to all the beloved creatures, present and past, who have shared their love and wisdom with us, while asking for nothing in return but to be a part of our family. And we are family, all the same color inside.

A special thanks to my human teachers; my wife, our children, grandchildren and the animals who have graced our lives over the years. It is no accident that a lifeline is three fourths feline and God spelled backwards is dog.

~Bernie S. Siegel, MD

## BERNIE S. SIEGEL, MD

Dr. Siegel, who prefers to be called Bernie, was born in Brooklyn, NY. He attended Colgate University and Cornell University Medical College where he graduated with honors. His surgical training took place at Yale New Haven Hospital, West Haven Veteran's Hospital, and the Children's Hospital of Pittsburgh. He is a former president of the American Holistic Medicine Association. In 1989 he retired from the practice of general and pediatric surgery to travel around the world, speaking to patients and their caregivers.

For many, Bernie needs no introduction as he has already touched many lives. In the late seventies he began talking about patient empowerment and the choice to live fully and die in peace. As a physician, who has cared for and counseled innumerable people whose mortality has been threatened by an illness, Bernie embraces a philosophy of living and dying that stands at the forefront of the medical ethics and spiritual issues our society grapples with today. In 1978, he originated Exceptional Cancer Patients, (http://ecap-online.org) a specific form of individual and group therapy utilizing patients' drawings, dreams, images, and feelings.

His first book, *Love, Medicine & Miracles* was published in 1986. This multi-million selling book was an 'event' that redirected his life. It was followed by *Peace, Love & Healing* and *How to Live Between Office Visits*. Bernie's realization that we all need help dealing with the difficulties of life, not just the physical ones, led to the writing of his fourth book *Prescriptions for Living*. Many books followed including, *Help Me to Heal, 365 Prescriptions for the Soul* and *101 Exercises for the Soul*. The debut of Bernie's first children's book, *Smudge Bunny* was followed by his latest book for parents entitled *Love, Magic & Mudpies - Raising Your Kids to Feel Loved, Be Kind, and Make a Difference*. *Faith, Hope, and Joy – The Unexpected Side Effects of Cancer* will be released early in 2009.

Bernie and his wife and coworker, Bobbie, live in a suburb of New Haven, Connecticut. They have five children and eight grandchildren. Bernie and Bobbie have co-authored their children, books, and articles. Their home, with its many children, pets and interests, often resembles a cross between a family art gallery, museum, zoo, and automobile repair shop. Bernie continues to pursue the breaking of new ground in the field of healing and personal growth, and to live and spread the message of kindness and love.

**www.berniesiegelmd.com**

## Bernie's Closing

There are so many wonderful poems and stories about animals as teachers and healers and I wish I could share them all with you. Many studies attest to the survival benefits of having a dog in your home, especially if you are confronted with a serious illness. In my new book, *Buddy's Candle*, Buddy teaches us how to accept life and death with grace and courage, and to use our precious limited time to serve the world in a meaningful way with love and joy.

As a surgeon who has worked with people with life threatening illnesses for years, I know the invaluable lessons we learn from our animals. My entire life I have felt very connected to animals. Fortunately my wife and I both feel the same way about animals, and we are always rescuing creatures.

When our five children were growing up, we had a good group of helpers and our home became a rescue site. We live on an acre and a half of land and broke every zoning law, but no one turned us in because everyone enjoyed our many creatures, and the neighbor's children learned to have a reverence for all life.

In closing let me share one last story. Years ago our dog Oscar had a type of cancer called a malignant melanoma. He was very sick and our veterinarian said he should be euthanized because he had never seen a dog this sick recover. When I went home and announced this to our children they said, "No, you don't put your patients to sleep and you're not putting Oscar to sleep." So I brought him home and spent time loving him, massaging him, sharing my meals and vitamins with him. In a few days he was on his feet and soon after that out the door playing with his siblings. He lived for years with no sign of cancer. My message to you all, which Oscar and our children confirmed for me, is how valuable is love, touch, and the ability of relationships to transform and heal us all.

I know there is a light in each of us by God's/Dog's design. We are all a part of the candle parade of light. As long as we remember to love, our candles will light up our lives.